PENGUIN BOOKS

1382

MAJOR THOMPSON LIVES IN FRANCE

PIERRE DANINOS

PIERRE DANINOS

MAJOR THOMPSON
LIVES IN FRANCE
and Discovers the French

*

With drawings by
WALTER GOETZ

PENGUIN BOOKS

Penguin Books Ltd, Harmondsworth, Middlesex
AUSTRALIA: Penguin Books Pty Ltd, 762 Whitehorse Road,
Mitcham, Victoria

—

First published in Great Britain by Jonathan Cape, 1955
Published in Penguin Books 1959

—

Translated from the French
Les Carnets du Major Thompson
by ROBIN FARN

Made and printed in Great Britain
by Wyman & Sons Ltd,
London Fakenham and Reading